# Practice Test 1
# for the OLSAT® (Level A)

# Otis-Lennon School Ability Test®
# Pre-K & Kindergarten (Level A)

## By Smart Cookie Ink

# INTRODUCTION

The *Otis-Lennon School Ability Test®* (*OLSAT®*) measures a student's reasoning and problem solving abilities using Verbal and Nonverbal approaches.

This test is administered to K–12 school children as a means to identify potentially gifted children for placement in accelerated learning programs. A good score on the OLSAT® qualifies a child for superior educational programs within public and private schools.

Analytical reasoning and problem solving are seldom part of the standard school curriculum. Most children appear for the OLSAT® without a clear understanding of what is expected of them. Sometimes even the brightest of young minds can be rattled because of unfamiliarity with the questions and test format. They are forced to respond reflexively in the absence of a test taking strategy.

Schools suggest a good night's sleep and a healthy breakfast as adequate preparation – as well-intended as this advice may be, it just won't cut it in this increasingly competitive environment.

**Help your child perform at his or her best AND ensure that his or her true potential is fairly and accurately evaluated!**

With this in mind, we have designed this book with a specific purpose: to hone your child's analytical reasoning and problem solving abilities that the Grade K OLSAT® test demands.

This book covers one full length Level A test for Pre-K and Kindergarten students. Pre-K and Kindergarten students take the same Level A test. However, Pre-K students answer 40 questions, whereas Kindergarten students answer 60 questions. Each practice test in this book has 60 questions.

The practice test that this book offers will
➢    Help tune your child's mind to think critically
➢    Provide varied exercises in all the areas of reasoning that the test considers:
   •Nonverbal
     *(Picture Classification, Picture Analogies, Picture Series, Figural Classification, Figural Analogies, Pattern Matrix, Figural Series)*
   • Verbal
     *(Following Directions, Aural Reasoning, Arithmetic Reasoning)*

➢    Familiarize your child with the format of the test.
In addition, the book also offers,
➢    Important test taking tips and strategies


# Now, get ready to ace this test!

# TABLE OF CONTENTS

 **HOW TO USE THIS BOOK**

## • PRACTICE ONE SECTION AT A TIME

The OLSAT® is divided into ten sections. Even though the actual test is administered in one sitting, while using the book for practice, it is recommended that the child gets introduced to the format one section at a time.

## • COMPLETE THE SAMPLE QUESTION

Each section has instructions and a sample question. It is recommended that the parent/test giver read the instructions in cursive writing to the child and do the question along with the child. This familiarizes the child with the format of the questions in that particular section.

Please note that some sections require the test giver to read each individual question in that section to the child. These questions are presented in a steep-slant cursive font to make them less readable for the child.

## • USE THE ANSWER KEY

Correct each section using the answer key. For any mistakes that may require further clarification, the answer key provides further explanation.

## • DISCUSS INCORRECT ANSWERS

Review the questions that the child may have gotten wrong. Discuss the question(s) and address the child's doubts using the answer key to further elucidate.

 # TIPS FOR TESTERS

## • A GOOD NIGHT'S SLEEP & A HEALTHY BREAKFAST IS KEY!

The test is administered in one sitting in most school districts and is usually about 60 minutes in length. Make sure the child gets a good night's sleep, eats a healthy breakfast and arrives to school on time on these important days of testing. Numerous studies have shown that a calm mind is significantly more capable of thinking clearly!

## • I said "LISTEN!"

Stress to the child just how important it is to listen carefully to and follow all instructions given to her/him during the examination. These instructions may include how to correctly fill in the test forms if it is, in fact, a paper-administered test.

As you already may know, the OLSAT® is divided into multiple sections. The child will be provided with directions at the start of each section. The directions will explain the section and tell him/her how the questions in that particular section should be answered. Ask the child to pay attention even though s/he may be familiar with the test format.

Sometimes, the questions within each section may be read aloud to the child instead of being provided in written form. If the questions are being read to the child, please remind him/her to focus and listen carefully AND emphasize that they **WILL NOT** be repeated! It is important that the child pays close attention to the reversing effect of negative words (e.g. NOT) or prefixes (e.g. un-).

## • WHAT IS IN YOUR MIND'S EYE?

Some children find it effective to first solve the question in their mind before looking at the answer choices. Introduce this approach at home and see if it works well for the child.

## • EVALUATE ALL ANSWER CHOICES!

Encourage the child to carefully evaluate ALL answer choices before choosing the answer which **BEST** answers the question. Remind the child that sometimes the best available answer may not be the most ideal answer or the answer in his/her mind. Ask the child to simply focus on what s/he considers the best of the lot!

## • SLASH THE TRASH!

It is never too early to teach children just how important the process of elimination is as a test-taking skill! If s/he can eliminate one or two obviously wrong answer choices at first glance, then more time can be effectively spent focusing in on picking the correct answer from among the remaining choices!

## • TAKE A GUESS!

Remember, OLSAT® scores are calculated based on the number of correct answers provided by the child. It is always best to answer **ALL** questions rather than leave any blank. If, after 'slashing the trash', the child is still unsure of the correct answer, ask her/him to guess from the remaining 'maybe' answers.

## • COLOR THE BUBBLE!

It is important for the child to know how to properly fill in/color bubbles if s/he is given a bubble test form. At other times, bubbles need to be colored in directly below the answer choices on the test itself, especially true for children in the First or Second Grade. Please keep in mind that children in pre-K and/or Kindergarten may only need to point at their answer choice. In any case, practice coloring bubbles and/or using a sample bubble test form depending on the child's age and grade level. Also, continue to remind the child to only color in one bubble per question. If the test is administered by computer, coloring bubbles doesn't come into play....it is just one easy click!

# Practice Test 1
# for the OLSAT® (Level A)

# Otis-Lennon School Ability Test®
# Pre-K & Kindergarten (Level A)

# PICTURE CLASSIFICATION

Look at the five pictures in each question. One of them is different from the other four and **does not** belong.

Color the bubble under the picture that **does not** belong.

# SAMPLE QUESTION

Read this to the child:

*Look! There are five pictures in this question. Four of the five pictures belong to the same family. One of them **does not** belong with the other four. Think about which picture is different from the other four pictures and why it is different.*

*Color the bubble under the picture that **does not** belong.*

ⓐ      ⓑ      ⓒ      ⓓ      ⓔ

*Answer: c*
*'c' does not belong with the other four pictures. The other four are flowers; 'c' is not a flower.*

**1.**

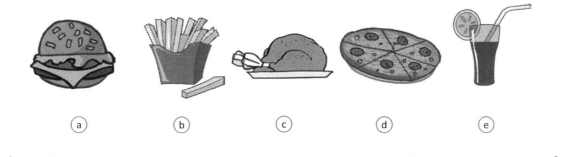

ⓐ     ⓑ     ⓒ     ⓓ     ⓔ

**2.**

ⓐ     ⓑ     ⓒ     ⓓ     ⓔ

**3.**

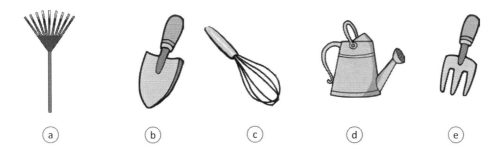

ⓐ     ⓑ     ⓒ     ⓓ     ⓔ

**4.**

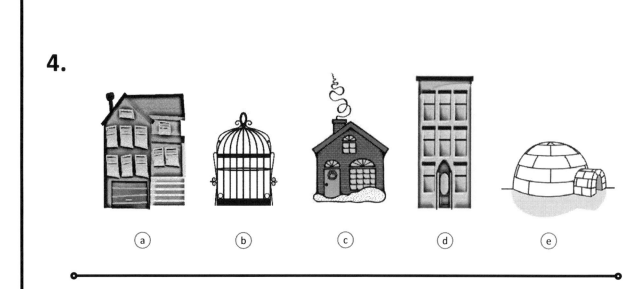

<table><tr><td>a</td><td>b</td><td>c</td><td>d</td><td>e</td></tr></table>

**5.**

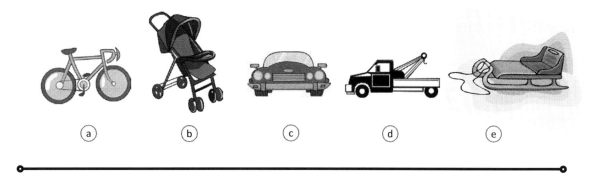

<table><tr><td>a</td><td>b</td><td>c</td><td>d</td><td>e</td></tr></table>

**6.**

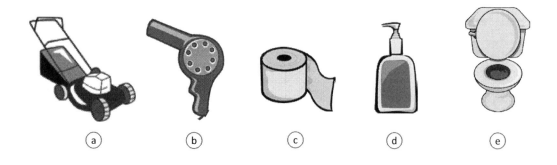

<table><tr><td>a</td><td>b</td><td>c</td><td>d</td><td>e</td></tr></table>

# PICTURE ANALOGIES

In the matrix given to you, determine the relationship between the pair of pictures on the top.

Pick a picture that completes the matrix in such a way that the bottom pair has the same relationship as the top pair. Color the bubble under your choice.

# SAMPLE QUESTION

Read this to the child:

*Look at the top two pictures! How are they related? Try to form a sentence in your mind with the top two pictures. For example, 'We get milk from a cow'. Now, try to form a similar sentence with the bottom picture. 'We get ......... from a chicken'. What would you fill in the blank with? Which picture would you choose so that the bottom pair has the same relationship as the top pair?*

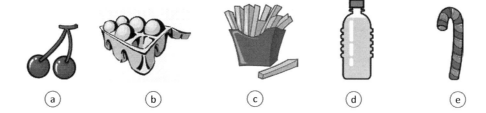

*Answer: b*
*We get eggs from a chicken.*

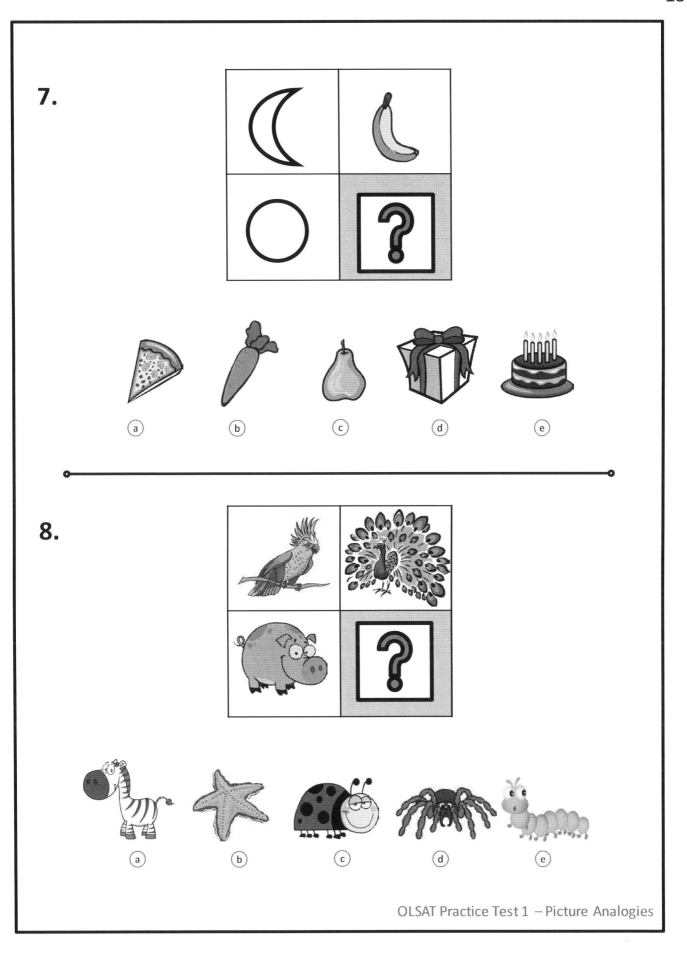

**7.**

**8.**

**9.**

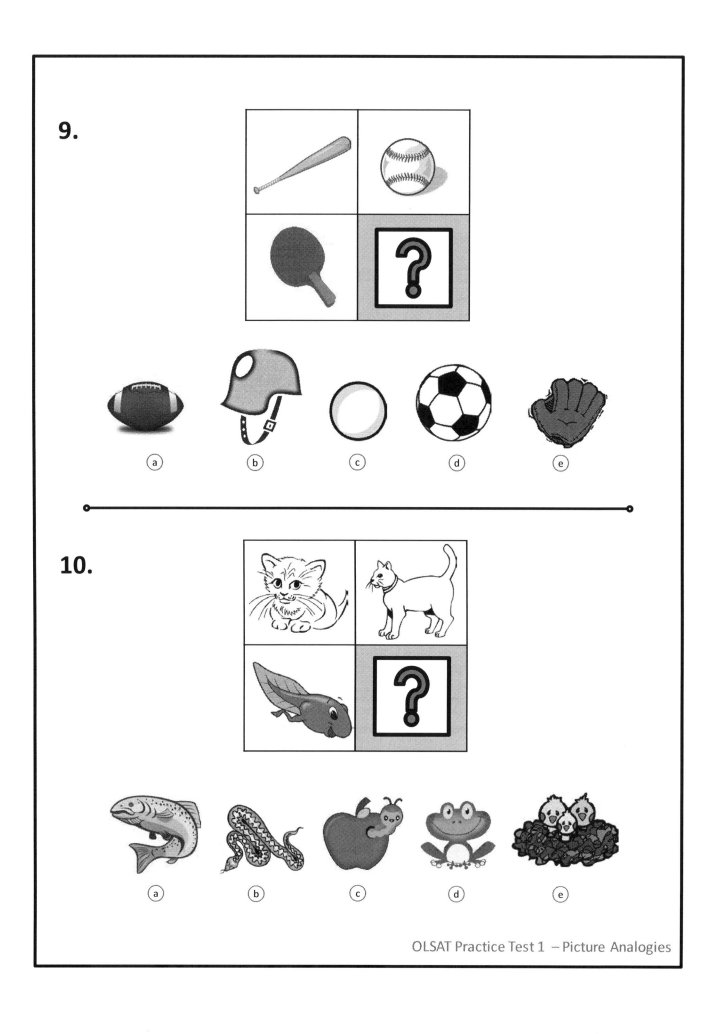

**10.**

**11.**

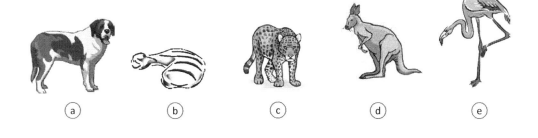

    (a)        (b)        (c)        (d)        (e)

**12.**

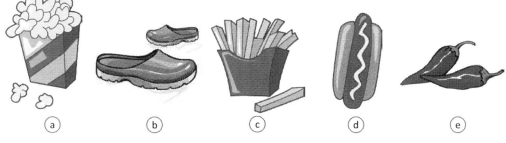

    (a)        (b)        (c)        (d)        (e)

# PICTURE SERIES

Pick the picture that completes the sequence provided by the other pictures in the question. Which picture comes next? Color the bubble under your choice.

# SAMPLE QUESTION

Read this to the child:

*Look! Below are pictures that follow a sequence, pattern or theme. They seem to belong to the same family and/or there is something similar happening to them. From the answer choices given to you, find the picture that will complete this sequence or pattern. What comes next OR what is missing?*

| (a) | (b) | (c) | (d) | (e) |

*Answer: a*

*The sequence shows the growing stages of a flowering plant.*

**13.**

**14.**

# FIGURE CLASSIFICATION

Look at the 5 images in each question. One of them is different from the other four and **does not** belong.

Color the bubble under the image that **does not** belong.

# SAMPLE QUESTION

Read this to the child:

*Look! There are five pictures in this question. Four of the five pictures belong to the same family. One of them does not belong with the other four. Think about which picture is different from the other four pictures and WHY it is different.*

*Color the bubble under the picture that does not belong.*

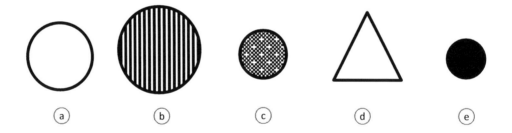

ⓐ     ⓑ     ⓒ     ⓓ     ⓔ

*Answer: d*
*'d' does not belong with the other four pictures. The other four are circles. 'd' is not a circle; it is a triangle.*

**15.**

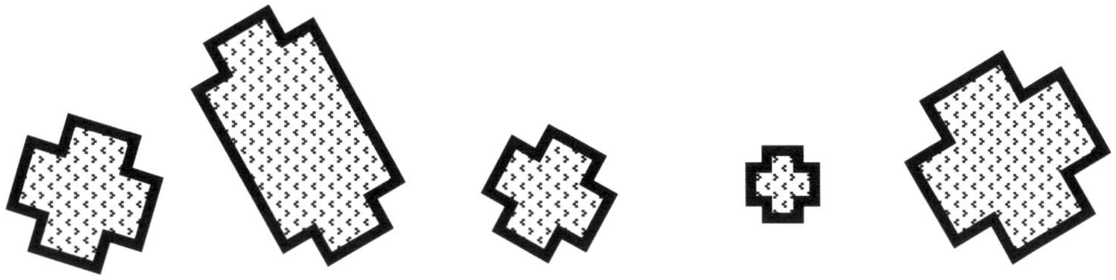

a      b      c      d      e

**16.**

a      b      c      d      e

**17.**

a      b      c      d      e

**18.**

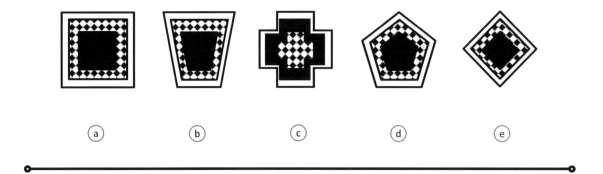

ⓐ      ⓑ      ⓒ      ⓓ      ⓔ

**19.**

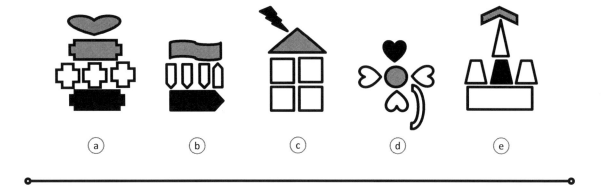

ⓐ      ⓑ      ⓒ      ⓓ      ⓔ

**20.**

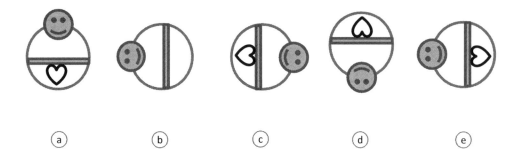

ⓐ      ⓑ      ⓒ      ⓓ      ⓔ

# FIGURE ANALOGIES

In the matrix given to you, determine the relationship between the pair of figures on the top.

Pick a figure that completes the matrix in such a way that the bottom pair has the same relationship as the top pair. Color the bubble under your choice.

# SAMPLE QUESTION

Read this to the child:

*Look at the two figures at the top of the picture below! How are they related? Try to form a sentence in your mind with the two figures on top. For example, 'The two figures on top have 4 sides each'. Now, try to form a similar sentence with the two figures on the bottom. The two figures on the bottom have 3 sides each.' Which answer would you choose so that the bottom pair has the same relationship as the top pair?*

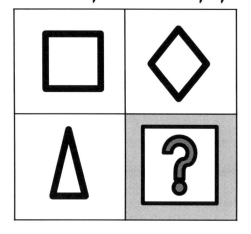

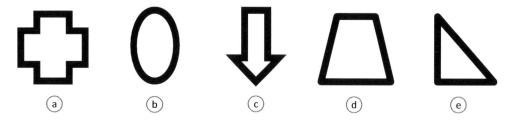

*Answer: e*
*'e' has three sides.*

**21.**

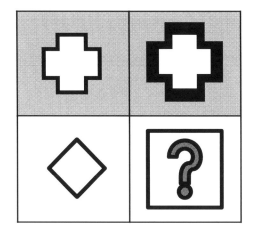

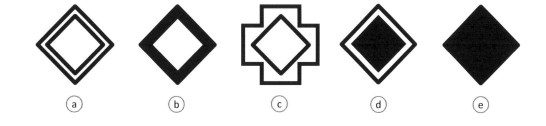

**22.**

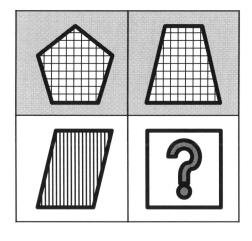

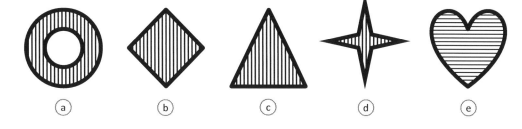

**23.**

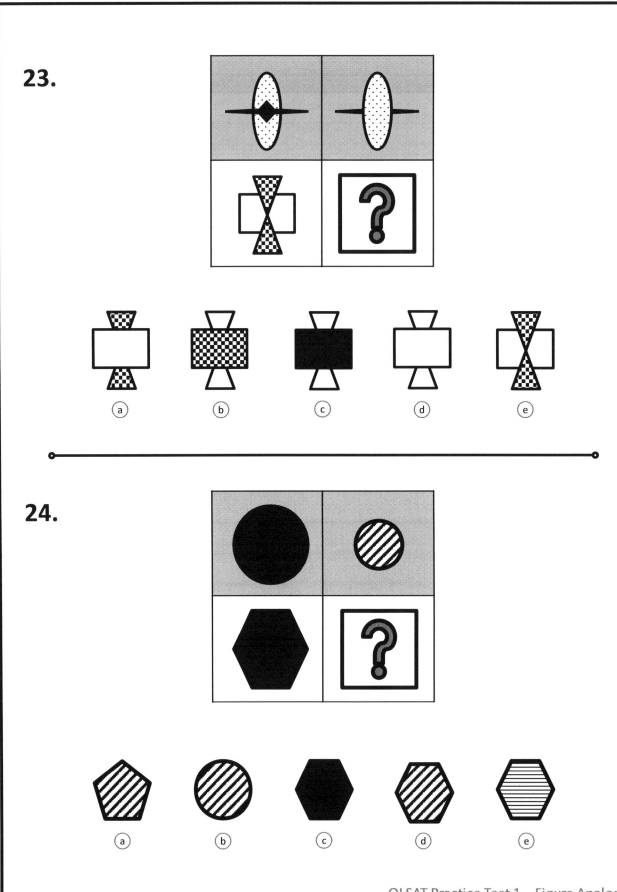

**25.**

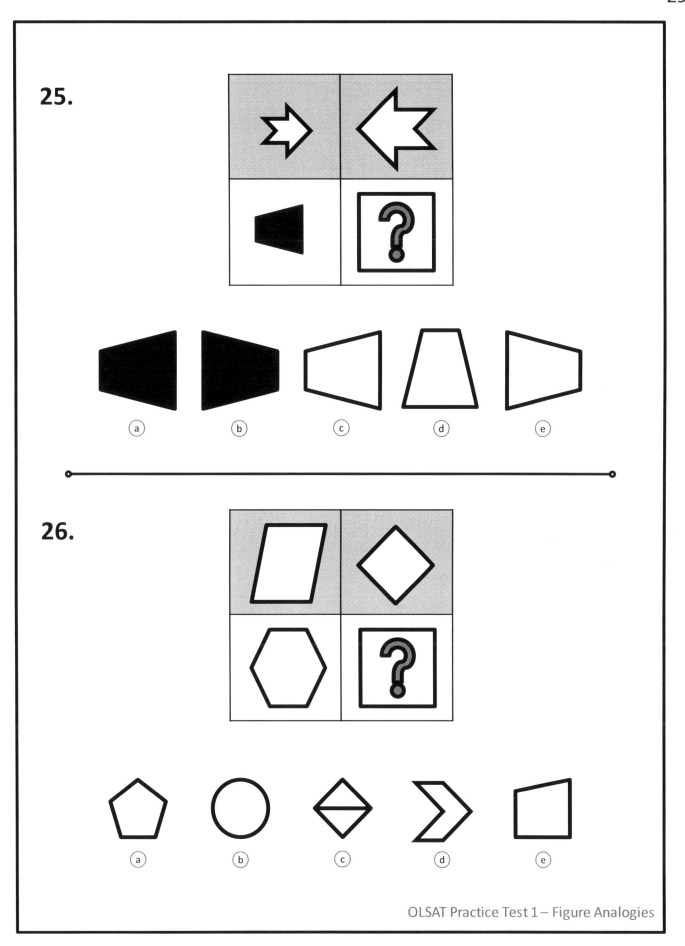

# PATTERN MATRIX

In this 3 by 3 matrix, the images change as you go across the row and down the column.

Pick the missing image that fits in the sequence and pattern of the other eight images and complete the matrix. Color the bubble under your choice.

# SAMPLE QUESTION

Read this to the child:

*Look! This question has three rows and three columns. Notice that the images change as you go across the row and down the column. Do you see a pattern? How are they related? Which answer would you choose to fit into the box with the question mark so that it completes the sequence or pattern?*

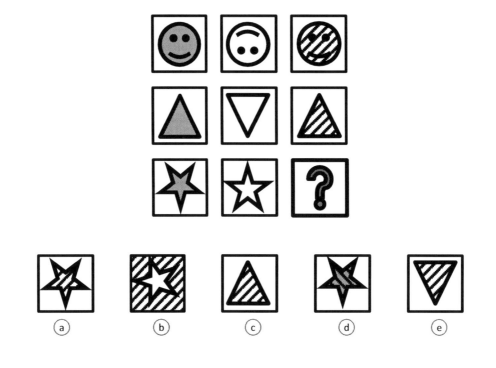

*Answer: a*

*Column 1 and Column 3 are similar except for the color and pattern. Column 2 is flipped.*

**27.**

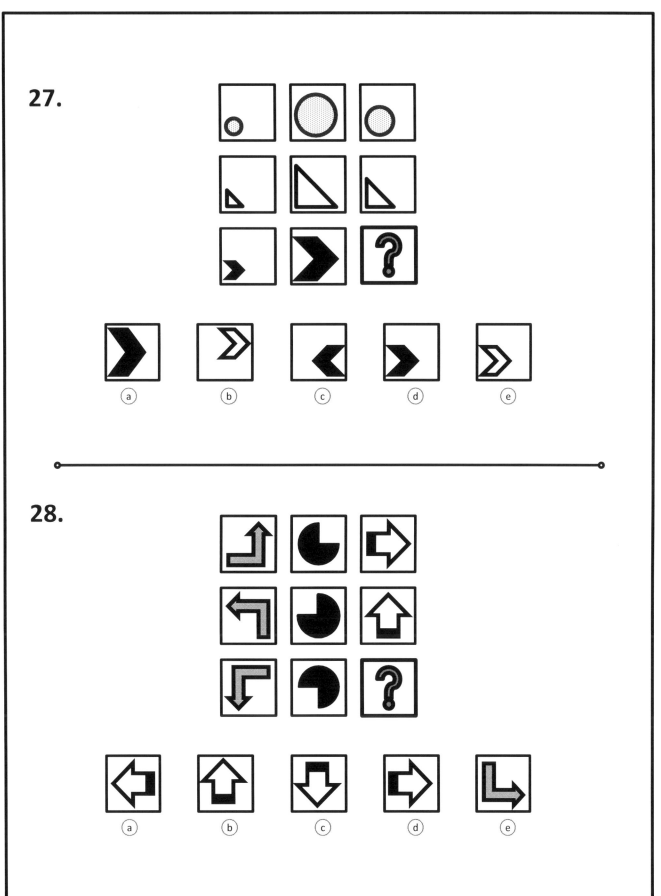

# FIGURAL SERIES

Pick the image that completes the pattern, theme or sequence in relation to the other images. Which image comes next?

Color the bubble under your choice.

# SAMPLE QUESTION

Read this to the child:

*Look! There are four figures that follow a sequence, pattern or theme. They seem to belong to the same family and/or there is something similar happening to them. From the answer choices given to you, find the figure that will complete this sequence or pattern. What comes next?*

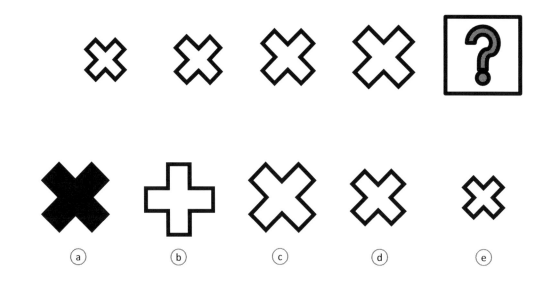

*Answer: c*
*The sequence goes from smallest to largest of the same shape in the same color.*

**29.**

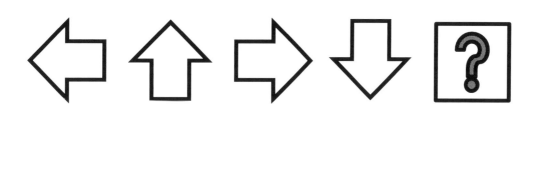

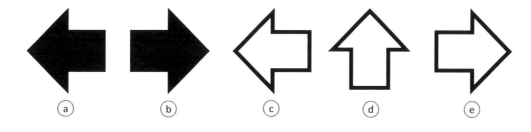

---

**30.**

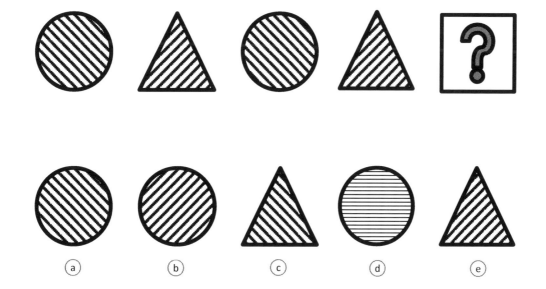

# FOLLOWING DIRECTIONS

Pick the picture that best answers the question by coloring the bubble under it.

## Note to parent/test-giver:

*The questions will not be provided in written form on the actual test. All questions in this section will be read to the child. For ease of use, this book will utilize a format where the questions are provided above the answer choices instead of on a separate page. However, they are in a steeply slanted cursive font to make them less readable for the child. For this section, please read the questions aloud to the child.*

# SAMPLE QUESTION

Read this to the child:

*For this section, it is very important that you listen carefully! I will read the question to you and you have to choose your answer. I will read the question once and only once, so, please make sure you listen carefully.*

*Select the picture that shows a cat UNDER the table.*

(a)

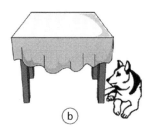

(b)

(c)

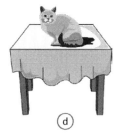

(d)

*Answer: a*
*'a' shows the cat under the table.*

**31.** *Select the picture that shows a circle to the right of a square.*

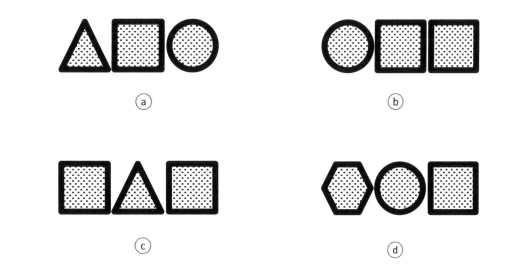

**32.** *Select the picture that shows a teddy bear in between two dinosaurs.*

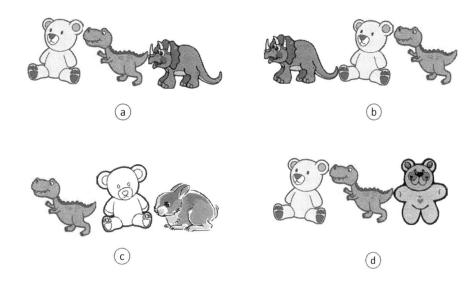

**33.** *Select the picture that shows a mouse on the cheese.*

ⓐ      ⓑ

ⓒ      ⓓ

**34.** *Select the picture that shows a small circle inside a large triangle.*

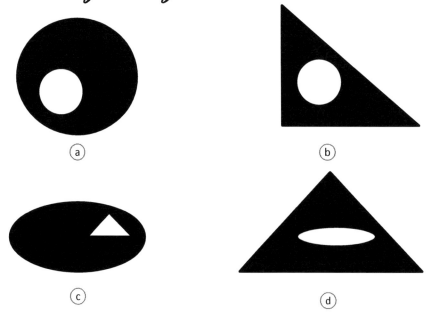

ⓐ      ⓑ

ⓒ      ⓓ

**35.** *Look at the pictures below. Which group has exactly 10 legs in total?*

**36.** *Select the picture that shows a sandwich, an apple and juice.*

**37.** *Look at the pictures below. Which group shows a pair of objects?*

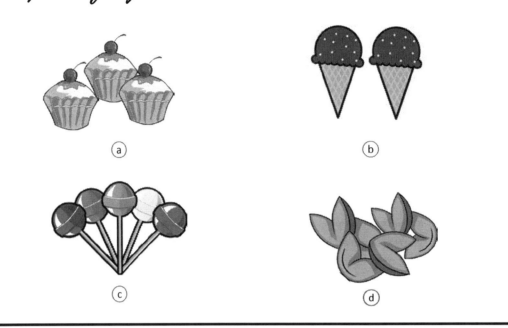

a

b

c

d

**38.** *Select the picture that has more than four corners.*

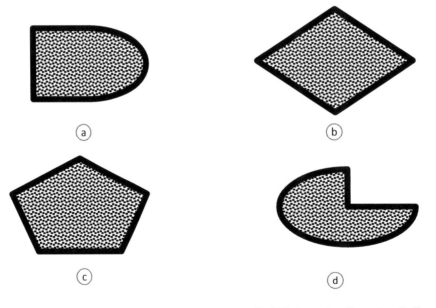

a

b

c

d

**39.** *Select the picture that shows a black heart inside white polygon.*

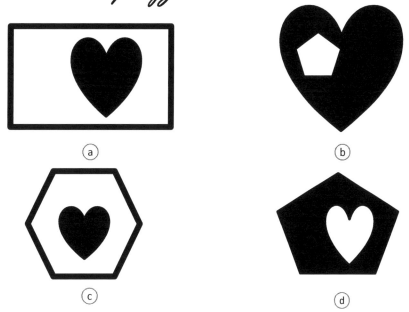

**40.** *Select the picture that shows exactly one vertical and two horizontal lines.*

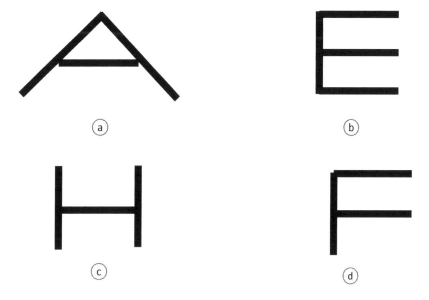

**41.** *Select the picture that shows a triangle on top of a striped rectangle.*

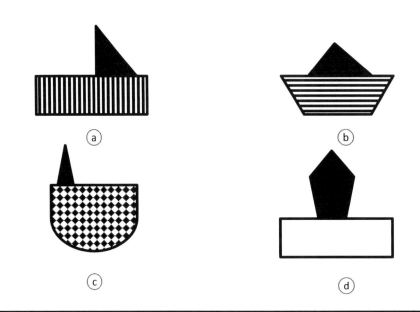

**42.** *Select the picture where the first number is 7, the second number is 5 and the third number is 1.*

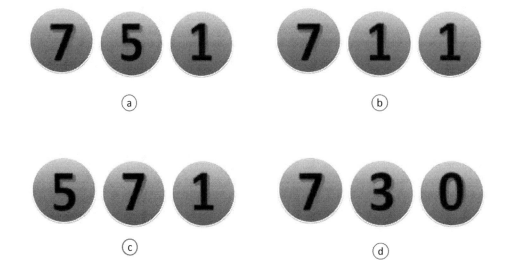

**43.** *Select the picture that shows 3 bananas and 2 pears.*

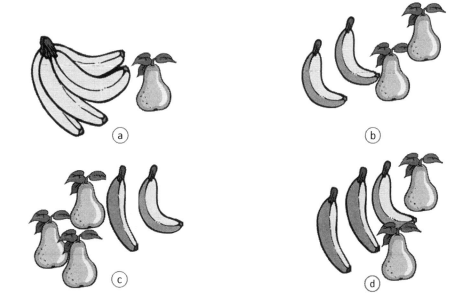

**44.** *Select the picture that shows one flying bird and two standing birds.*

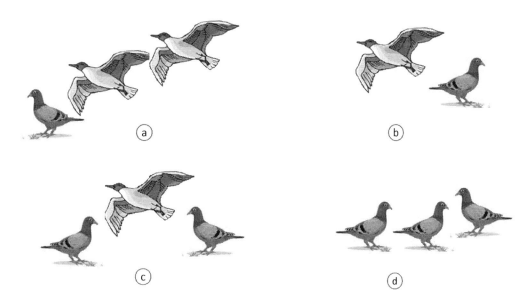

# AURAL REASONING

Pick the picture that best answers the question by coloring the bubble under it.

**Note to parent/test-giver:**

*The questions will not be provided in written form on the actual test. All questions in this section will be read to the child. For ease of use, this book will utilize a format where the questions are provided above the answer choices instead of on a separate page. However, they are in a steeply slanted cursive font to make them less readable for the child. For this section, please read the questions aloud to the child.*

# SAMPLE QUESTION

Read this to the child:

*For this section, it is very important that you listen carefully! I will read the question to you and you have to choose your answer. I will read the question once and only once, so, please make sure you listen carefully.*

*Tracy takes a backpack to school everyday. Which one of these things will Tracy most probably NOT carry in her backpack?*

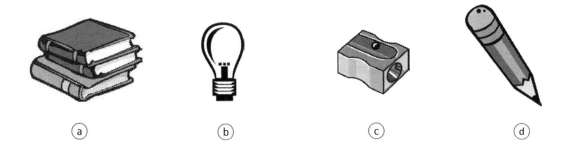

<table>
<tr><td>ⓐ</td><td>ⓑ</td><td>ⓒ</td><td>ⓓ</td></tr>
</table>

*Answer: b*
*Tracy is least likely to carry a lightbulb in her backpack.*

**45.**

Which one of these would you most likely not find in a kitchen?

(a)        (b)        (c)        (d)

---

**46.**

Which one of these vegetables grows below the ground?

(a)        (b)        (c)        (d)

**47.**

Which one of these pictures shows a boy flying a kite?

a      b      c      d

**48.**

Which one of these animals lives only in water and not on land?

a      b      c      d

**49.**

When Danny gets back from school, he first has a snack and then goes out to play. After playtime, he takes a bath. What does Danny do as soon as he gets back from school?

a      b      c      d

**50.**

Mike gave his mother a single rose for Mother's day. Which one of these shows what Mike gifted his mother?

a      b      c      d

**51.**

Which one of these is not a mammal?

    ⓐ        ⓑ        ⓒ        ⓓ

---

**52.**

Joshua and Jack are ready to go to the pool.
Which one of these would they wear to see
better under water?

    ⓐ        ⓑ        ⓒ        ⓓ

**53.**

It is snowing outside and Marie wants to build a snowman. Which one of these will she probably not need to decorate her snowman?

(a)　　　　(b)　　　　(c)　　　　(d)

**54.**

Sandra is very thirsty after playing tag with her friends. Which one of these would she reach out for to quench her thirst?

(a)　　　　(b)　　　　(c)　　　　(d)

# ARITHMETIC REASONING

Pick the picture that best answers the question by coloring the bubble under it.

**Note to parent/test-giver:**

*The questions will not be provided in written form on the actual test. All questions in this section will be read to the child. For ease of use, this book will utilize a format where the questions are provided above the answer choices instead of on a separate page. However, they are in a steeply slanted cursive font to make them less readable for the child. For this section, please read the questions aloud to the child.*

# SAMPLE QUESTION

Read this to the child:

*For this section, it is very important that you listen carefully! I will read the question to you and you have to choose your answer. I will read the question once and only once, so, please make sure you listen carefully.*

*Jack had 1 pig and 2 sheep in his farm. His dad bought him 2 more pigs. How many pigs and sheep does Jack have now?*

      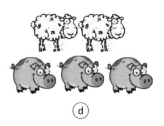

     ⓐ            ⓑ            ⓒ            ⓓ

*Answer: d*
*Jack will have 3 (1+2) pigs and 2 sheep.*

**55.** *Count how many squares there are in the top picture. Which one of the pictures below has 2 fewer squares than the picture above?*

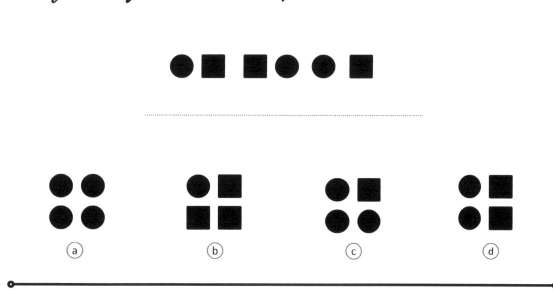

ⓐ      ⓑ      ⓒ      ⓓ

**56.** *Lani had 4 strawberries and 6 cherries in her snack box. She gave her friend Stacy 2 cherries and 2 strawberries. How many strawberries and cherries did Lani have for herself?*

ⓐ      ⓑ      ⓒ      ⓓ

**57.** *Look at the number on the top. Which one of the numbers below is 2 more than the number on the top.*

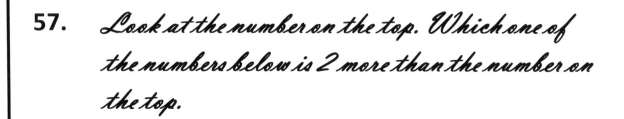

3

---

1     3     5     6

(a)     (b)     (c)     (d)

---

**58.** *Count how many white circles there are in the top picture. Which one of the pictures below has 2 more white circles than the picture above?*

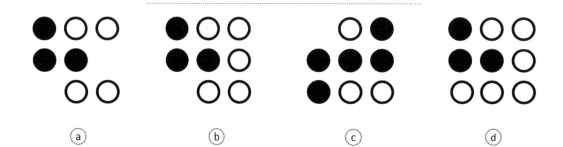

(a)     (b)     (c)     (d)

**59.** *Look at the candy canes in the top picture. If the candy canes are shared equally between 2 children, how many candy canes will each child get?*

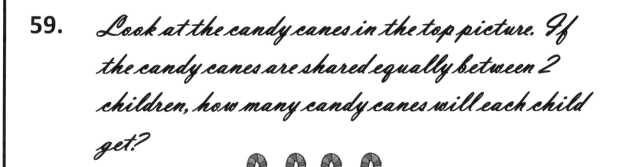

    (a)          (b)          (c)          (d)

**60.** *Count how many apples and bananas there are in the top picture. If 2 apples and 2 bananas are eaten, what would be left?*

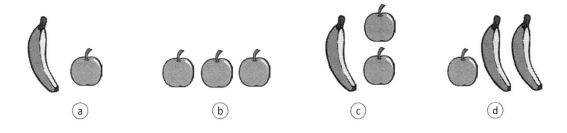

    (a)          (b)          (c)          (d)

# ANSWER KEY

# OLSAT® Practice Test 1 – *Answer Key*

| | | |
|---|---|---|
| 1. e | 21. b | 41. a |
| 2. c | 22. c | 42. a |
| 3. c | 23. a | 43. d |
| 4. b | 24. d | 44. c |
| 5. e | 25. b | 45. b |
| 6. a | 26. d | 46. c |
| 7. e | 27. d | 47. d |
| 8. a | 28. a | 48. d |
| 9. c | 29. c | 49. c |
| 10. d | 30. a | 50. a |
| 11. c | 31. a | 51. c |
| 12. a | 32. b | 52. b |
| 13. a | 33. c | 53. d |
| 14. c | 34. b | 54. b |
| 15. b | 35. d | 55. c |
| 16. d | 36. b | 56. d |
| 17. e | 37. b | 57. c |
| 18. c | 38. c | 58. b |
| 19. a | 39. c | 59. c |
| 20. b | 40. d | 60. b |

# OLSAT® Practice Test 1
## *Answer Key with Explanation*

1. e

   The beverage does not belong with the foods.

2. c

   The reptile does not belong with the mammals.

3. c

   The kitchen utensil does not belong with the garden tools.

4. b

   The cage does not belong with the human dwellings.

5. e

   The sled does not belong with the wheeled vehicles.

6. a

   The lawn mower does not belong with the things found in a bathroom.

7. e

   The banana is crescent in shape. The cake is round in shape.

8. a

   The animals on the top are birds. The animals on the bottom are mammals.

9. c

   Baseball bat goes with the baseball. The table tennis racket goes with the ping-pong ball.

10. d

    Kittens become cats. Tadpoles turn into frogs.

11. c

    The animals on the top are dogs. The animals on the bottom are wild cats.

12. a

    Cheese is made with milk. Popcorn is made with corn kernels.

# OLSAT® Practice Test 1
## *Answer Key with Explanation*

## 13. a

Sequence from egg to chicken.

## 14. c

Steps to making a glass of lemonade.

## 15. b

Same shape ( same proportions); Different sizes.

## 16. d

Two black circles and two identical   patterned shapes.

## 17. e

Four sided figures.

## 18. c

Shapes with the outer shape in white, the middle in pattern and the inner in black.

## 19. a

 A picture made up of 6 shapes – 4 white, 1 black and 1 grey.

## 20. b

Same picture rotated.

## 21. b

Same shape with a thick black outline.

## 22. c

Number of sides minus one; Shaded similarly.

# OLSAT® Practice Test 1
## *Answer Key with Explanation*

**23.** a

Foreground images goes to background. Background images comes to foreground.

**24.** d

Decrease in size, change from black to shaded.

**25.** b

Increase in size; flip.

**26.** d

Same number of sides.

**27.** d

Small, large and medium of the same shape/ same color placed similarly in the bottom left corner.

**28.** a

Rotation of the same shape in a counter clockwise direction down the column.

**29.** c

Rotation of the same shape in a clockwise direction.

**30.** a

Pattern with alternating circle and triangle shaded with upward diagonal lines.

**31.** a

'a' shows a circle to the right of a square.

**32.** b

'b' shows a teddy bear in between two dinosaurs.

# OLSAT® Practice Test 1
## *Answer Key with Explanation*

### 33. c

'c' shows a mouse on the cheese.

### 34. b

'b' shows a small circle inside a large triangle.

### 35. d

The group of animals in 'd' has exactly 10 legs in total.

### 36. b

'b' shows a sandwich, an apple and a juice.

### 37. b

'b' shows a pair of objects.

### 38. c

'c' has five corners.

### 39. c

'c' shows a black heart inside a white polygon.

### 40. d

'd' has exactly one vertical and two horizontal lines.

### 41. a

'a' shows a triangle on top of a striped rectangle.

### 42. a

'a' has the first number as 7, second as 5 and third as 1.

# OLSAT® Practice Test 1
## *Answer Key with Explanation*

### 43. d

'd' shows three bananas and 2 pears.

### 44. c

'c' shows one flying bird and 2 standing birds.

### 45. b

Toothbrush and toothpaste will most likely not be found in a kitchen.

### 46. c

Carrots grow below the ground.

### 47. d

'd' shows a boy flying a kite.

### 48. d

Seahorses live only in water and not on land.

### 49. c

Danny has a snack as soon as he gets back from school.

### 50. a

Mike gave his mother a single rose stem.

### 51. c

Penguins are not mammals.

### 52. b

Joshua and Jack will need goggles to see under water in a pool.

# OLSAT® Practice Test 1
## *Answer Key with Explanation*

## 53. d

Marie will most probably not need a fish to decorate her snowman.

## 54. b

Sandra will reach for the bottle of water to quench her thirst.

## 55. c

'c' has 2 fewer squares than the picture.

## 56. d

After giving out 2 strawberries and 2 cherries, Lani will have 2 strawberries and 4 cherries left.

## 57. c

'5' is 2 more than '3'.

## 58. b

'b' has 5 (3+2) white circles.

## 59. c

Each child will get 2 candy canes.

## 60. b

There will be 3 apples left. .

Made in the USA
Middletown, DE
11 November 2018